Mediterranean Diet Cookbook for Beginners

Burn Fat with Easy Recipes to Fix Your Wrong Habits.

Boost Your Metabolism, Lose Weight with Healthy Lifestyle.

Tania Frei

TABLE OF CONTENTS

The information provided herein is stated to be truthful and consistent, in that any liability, in terms of inattention or otherwise, by any usage or abuse of any policies, processes, or directions contained within is the solitary and utter responsibility of the recipient reader. Under no circumstances will any legal responsibility or blame be held against the publisher for any reparation, damages, or monetary loss due to the information herein, either directly or indirectly.

INTRODUCTION

Healthy living is a treasured luxury that doesn't come by itself. You have to schedule it. Nutrition plays a crucial role in supplying the body with essential nutrients for growth and development. While some foods are considered healthy and in large quantities are required, others may be excluded from a daily diet. So works a Mediterranean diet plan.

The most common type of healthy diet is the Mediterranean diet. Studies have proved that people in the Mediterranean region can attribute the secret of healthy living to their balanced diet and active lifestyles. Researches have also shown that not only does this diet alleviate chronic heart disease, it also increases life expectancy.

Today's habits show that most people prefer to eat fried, frozen, or tinned foods that contain saturated fats and sugar. Lifestyles often suggest that most people don't take the time to exercise. As a result, with an increased chance of heart disease, diabetes and cancers, many people are obese and unhealthy.

The Mediterranean diet plan does not reduce the food types that one eats. The diet advises wise choices regarding food. For starters, instead of tinned and frozen food, one should eat fresh fruit and vegetables. The food plan is based on the pyramid Mediterranean diet. According to him, cereals, grains, pasta, vegetables, legumes, beans, fruit, and nuts are food products to be included in a daily diet. These nutritious goods are a rich source of carbohydrates, fabrics, vitamins, minerals, and proteins. The recommended milk, yogurt and cheese consumption, low to moderate, reduce excessive intake of saturated fats. Animal meat such as chicken and eggs shall be consumed regularly and red meat, several times a month. Fish is considered a better choice, since it is high in nutritional value.

Olive oil provides good fat, which is responsible for reducing blood cholesterol levels and maintaining a healthy heart. All these recommendations are in line with a regular diet recommendation in the Mediterranean diet plan. A balanced dietary intake through an active physical life. This is not to say that people did not find time to rest in the Mediterranean area. They also used the time to relax and socialize after each meal, unwillingly giving time for proper digestion and good health.

CHAPTER ONE

Understanding the Mediterranean diet

The Mediterranean diet is one of the propagated diets, but that many people still don't know. It is usually a very simple diet and one of the most suitable, since it involves small risks to health.

Your idea is very simple and clear, and you always get interesting results done in a correct and specified way. It is from this transition that you will achieve your goal of a healthy weight loss, always with a consistent schedule.

Let's bring about what it treats for those who don't know about this diet, and also other factors that may enhance its action. From this, you can change your reality in favor of a type of diet that is very appropriate even for those who don't seek weight loss themselves. The Mediterranean diet includes a large number of fruits, vegetables, beans, nuts, seeds, bread and other cereals. In the Mediterranean diet, fruits and vegetables are usually grown locally. Raw or minimally processed fruits and vegetables are often consumed. Fruit and vegetables contain many essential vitamins and minerals as well as antioxidants which are essential for good health.

The primary source of fat for the Mediterranean Diet is the use of monounsaturated fat. Olive oil is monounsaturated fat which is a rich antioxidant source like vitamin E. Olive oil is used as an alternative to butter, margarine and other fats. Butter and cream in fact are used only on special occasions. In the Mediterranean diet, olive oil is used for cooking tomato sauces, vegetable dishes, salads, and frying fish.

What is the Mediterranean diet

The Mediterranean diet is a set of human-related skills, knowledge, practices and traditions, ranging from land to table, covering crops, crops and fishing, as well as preserving, processing and preparing food and, in particular, its consumption.

This diet's nutritional model has remained constant over time and space, with the main ingredients being olive oil, cereals, fresh or dried fruits and vegetables, a moderate proportion of meat, fish and dairy products, abundant condiments and wine or infusions accompanying their consumption at the table, always respecting the beliefs of each community.

The Mediterranean diet-whose name derives from the Greek word regular, which means the way of life-comprises not only food, as it is a cultural element that promotes social interaction, verifying that traditional meals are a cornerstone of customs celebrations and festive events. Additionally, the Mediterranean diet gave rise to a large body of knowledge, poems, choruses, tales and legends.

One of the few diets that affect the health of those who adopt it is the Mediterranean diet. As you'll know a little later, this isn't even a diet, but rather a lifestyle that can be practiced for life.

When we think about diets, thoughts about poverty, hunger and the intake of tasteless foods always come to mind. That should not however be the case. Diet is a diet in which we choose to focus on eating other foods while limiting or reducing the consumption of others. Dieting is a diet that can aim for weight loss as well as weight gain. In addition to reducing weight, the diet may also aim to improve the symptoms of a variety of medical conditions that are closely related to food. These include, for example, type 2 diabetes, high cholesterol, high blood pressure, metabolic syndrome and even cancer.

When we want to follow a particular diet or diet to improve our health, the changes we make must be long-term. The Mediterranean Diet is one long-term diet. Not even a diet; it is a diet that we choose to follow for a long time or for life.

History of the Mediterranean diet

In recent years, there has been increasing concern for their health among men and women in different countries around the world. Many men and women often paid more attention to their meals, as many people were more concerned with their general health. Both men and women basically make dietary choices to boost their overall health and wellbeing.

A significant number of these men and women became interested in the Mediterranean diet as people became more aware of their health and nutrition. Yes, if you're a person who appreciates the food-health relationship, you may have a keen interest in the history of the Mediterranean diet.

Before you can fully understand what the Mediterranean diet is all about, you have to be mindful that it is more of a philosophy than a single eating regimen. There is in fact no Mediterranean diet popular to all Mediterranean countries around the world. Instead, the "Mediterranean Diet" consists of the foods that people consume together in the different nations of the region.

The Origins of the Mediterranean Diet

The concept of a Mediterranean diet derives from the eating habits and patterns of the people who populate Italy, Greece, Spain, France, Tunisia, Lebanon and Morocco. As a result, the Mediterranean diet also includes a huge variety of delicious foods. In reality, if a person chooses to embrace the Mediterranean dining scheme definition, or if a person chooses to pursue a Mediterranean diet system, he or she will have the ability to enjoy a vast range of scrumptious food.

The diet of the peoples who populated the Mediterranean Sea regions has, in fact, remained almost unchanged for well over a thousand years. The region's history is full of examples of men and women living longer than similarly situated people consuming alternate diets. Through the centuries, people in the Mediterranean Sea region have enjoyed longer lives at the same historical epoch than people in other parts of the world.

Foods and beverages which are indigenous to the geographic landmass surrounding the Mediterranean Sea are at the heart of the Mediterranean diet. In short, the development of the Mediterranean diet and dining pattern developed initially by providential. The region's people ate those foods naturally and understandably, and drank those beverages that were readily available in and around their homes.

Historical elements of the Mediterranean diet scheme

As already mentioned, the diet of the Mediterranean Sea region's peoples has remained essentially unchanged over the centuries. The Mediterranean diet is made up of a plethora of healthy food items including:

- Fresh fruit
- Fresh vegetables

- Low-fat nuts
- Whole grains
- Monounsaturated fat

The Mediterranean diet used by people for generation after generation, in a similar vein, excludes or limits certain food items that have been deemed harmful in recent scientific studies. These food items are less than desirable and include:

- Saturated fats
- Red and fatty meat
- Rich dairy products
- Fatty fish

The so-called Mediterranean diet is the historical evolution of the Mediterranean Sea basin through generations of cultures and civilizations.

Man learns to grow certain plant species 10,000 years ago, and domesticates certain animals, ceases to be nomadic and creates stable population settlements, usually in areas with good climate and water.

Nutrition is already expressed in many texts in the ancient civilizations of Babylon and Egypt. We make observations about foods that should or should not be eaten and one of them is also forbidden.

The basin of the Mediterranean is a crossroads of nations, languages, cultures, and religions. With various eating practices, diets, fasts, ritual meals, etc. Driven by Christianity, Judaism, and Islam.

The Greeks, Punics, and Romans entered the Mediterranean with wheat, vineyards, and olive trees.

The Germans the rice, citrus, eggplant and dried pasta Muslims butter.

American basic foods were imported from America, such as tomatoes, peppers, and potatoes.

Based on a natural balance of fish and vegetable meats, with plenty of fiber, few saturated fats, this slow and continuous sum of products has given rise to the now commonly called Mediterranean diet. Carbohydrates of fast and slow absorption with ample vitamins and unsaturated fats and complemented with minerals and trace elements.

The Mediterranean was the melting pot of cultures and cuisines, where everything was added. Nothing has stood out and the sun and sea have provided the strong diversity and variety It is a healthy, balanced and highly valued cuisine or diet.

Hopkin (English) together with Fujian, the 1931 Nobel Prize, found out what the essential components of a complete diet should be, and that there are other components such as vitamins that are part of the diet. In the early twentieth century, advances in nutrition went faster than other sciences, seeking the welfare of the population.

Scientifically today the so-called Mediterranean diet is considered to be an excellent model of the role.

The Science behind the Mediterranean Diet

The cardiac disease had become a serious health problem at the turn of the 20th century. At that time, researchers studying the disease and its causes discovered a startling pattern: the incidence of heart problems was much lower in some Mediterranean countries, particularly Italy and Greece compared to America.

The basis of the Mediterranean diet

The explanation they postulated might be in their diet: rich in plants, including fruits, vegetables, whole grains, legumes, potatoes, nuts and seeds. A strong quantity of extra virgin olive oil and a modest quantity of fish, poultry, dairy and eggs, as well as red meat, rarely completed this tradition's foundation.

The scientific and nutritional Interest in it is relatively recent and, like so many other items on this subject, it's supposed advantages have become almost magical forces due to the inflated word of mouth and tricky publicity.

How does the Mediterranean diet work?

A fiber-rich mixed diet with healthy fats and numerous fresh ingredients such as vegetables, Mediterranean salads, fish and fresh fruit should make our body slim. The Mediterranean diet scores with many important ingredients controlling blood lipids and reducing the risk of heart disease. Quite healthy for digestion are vegetables, fruits and salads. The menu also includes pasta, pizza, rice, legumes, cold-pressed olive oil, fresh herbs, and garlic.

The Mediterranean diet program is important: take the time to eat. So it is very important to have a slow and comfortable meal. It takes a lot of time for the Southern Europeans to cook and eat with great pleasure. Smart tactic-now studies have shown this as well: slow eating helps you lose weight. Because if you don't take your time, you also skip the natural feeling of satiety on your body and thus eat more calories unnecessarily.

Mediterranean diet also maintains healthy fat metabolism and reduces the cholesterol levels according to studies. Additionally, scientific research shows a positive correlation between the Mediterranean diet and the prevention of Alzheimer's. A US study has shown that foods such as vegetables, fruit, olive oil and the like can lower the risk of Alzheimer's disease.

The Mediterranean diet does not provide for a supplementary sports program. Calorie counting is not the order of the day, either-you can get enough of the right food. It should always be prepared freshly in the best case.

CHAPTER TWO

Living longer with a Mediterranean diet

The Mediterranean diet, supplemented with virgin olive oil or nuts such as nuts, hazelnuts and almonds, is more effective in preventing cardiovascular diseases than low-fat diets of all kinds.

We live in a society that is obsessed with seeking the elixir of eternal youth, but there is an inexorable biological reality: we are oxidizing and that is why our bodies are aging. It is up to us to faster or slower than this oxidation. There are no miracles. It is possible to live longer and in better health conditions, as long as we are willing to change certain habits.

People who adhere to a healthy diet like the traditional Mediterranean would be more likely to prevent depression, so nutrition could help treat that mental disorder, suggests an international team of researchers.

Public health, psychiatry, and nutrition specialists evaluated the role of dietary interventions in depression with the intention of developing recommendations for future psychiatric health care, as the disorder carries high social costs.

The researchers conducted a systematic review of indices and results from 41 longitudinal and cross-sectional studies on healthy diet compliance with depressive symptoms or clinical depression, which attempted to synthesize the link between food quality and disorder.

The researchers from the United Kingdom, France, Australia and Spain conclude that a diet based on fruits, vegetables, grains, fish, nuts and olive oil, but without too much meat or dairy, seems to have advantages in terms of mood.

Dr. Camille Lasalle of University College London points out the evidence that the food we eat can make a difference in reducing our risk of depression.

Experts in metabolic medicine say more rigorous and specific trials are needed to confirm evidence of the possible connection and determine whether depression can be treated with diet.

In fact it is complicated to explain the link between mood and food, as there are many factors that may be involved.

Depression can cause loss of appetite and someone who feels bad cannot take care of it as well, while happy people can be more likely to lead healthier lifestyles, including not drinking alcohol is a depressing mood known to them.

Eating bad foods, lots of sugar and highly processed foods may increase the risk of depression, which means eliminating them from the diet is important.

Research on the traditional Mediterranean diet has shown that it can reduce our risk of developing diseases like type 2 diabetes, hypertension and high cholesterol, all of which are risk factors for cardiac diseases.

The researchers have discovered that people closely following a Mediterranean diet would live longer and have less chance of gaining weight.

Health Benefits of the Mediterranean Diet

1. Lower risk of heart disease

Olive oil is the main ingredient in cooking and Mediterranean flavor. Olive oil contains monounsaturated fats, which for a healthy heart are a good component. In comparison, eating foods high in saturated fat leads to heart disease growth. Instead of butter, many Mediterranean dishes are cooked with oil and sauces and dressings include olive oil as one of the principal ingredients.

Mix various types of balsamic spoonfuls of vinegar with oil-of whatever flavor you like and you'll get a healthy salad dressing. There's no need to buy premixed dressings filled with unnecessary fats when you can create a healthy one with just a few ingredients, simply and easily. Therefore, the fresher it is, the better and a delicious salad dressing is produced if you use a little olive oil and balsamic vinegar.

2. Lower risk of having diabetes

Olive oil has many benefits for the skin. Since Mediterranean diets use it in different ways, if you follow the diet to the letter, you'll surely benefit from it. Some research studies have shown that olive oil and the Mediterranean diet, in particular, could help reduce the risk of developing type 2 diabetes.

Researchers believe a large number of rich minerals and phytochemicals in the Mediterranean diet can decrease insulin resistance and inflammation. Your body needs to successfully break down the sugars. If the body can't do this properly, the risk of suffering from type 2 diabetes could be greater.

3. Prevents hypertension

All you consume directly affects your blood pressure and there are foods in the Mediterranean diet that can help lower the pressure. Additionally, this diet consists of healthy foods that don't increase blood pressure. Genetics can play an important role in whether or not you have hypertension although it is not very good to have an unhealthy diet that contains a lot of fat and salt.

Unnecessary sodium will not be consumed in the Mediterranean diet by not eating processed foods which will increase blood pressure and hold it at very high levels. Hypertension can cause hypertension and other cardiovascular diseases so this diet can help you to reduce the serious health risks involved.

4. Prevents fatty liver disease

A diet rich in processed foods that contain salt, sugar, calories and unhealthy fats is practiced by many people. Adopting such an unhealthy diet increases the risk of developing obesity, which is the main cause of fatty liver disease. The amount of olive oil in the Mediterranean diet helps to remove many saturated fats from the diet and, at the same time, prevents fatty liver diseases.

Interestingly, the diet does not include red meat, as it contains a lot of saturated fat. Alternatively, mineral-rich chicken and fish are the meats preferred by this diet. Everything you eat and how much you eat of something the liver has difficulty processing (such as red meat) can lead to other liver diseases.

5. A potentially longer lifespan

Some studies link longevity with the Mediterranean diet. Diet can also reduce the risk of cardiovascular disease, which ultimately helps people live longer lives. Then start eating more fresh produce, nuts, seeds and olive oil to reap health benefits, including the possibility of living longer and reducing the chances of heart problems. While it is obviously desirable to start and maintain this diet in youth throughout life, research has shown that it can also have a positive effect on those who start eating it in later life.

6. Improvement of cognitive function

The research suggests a correlation between the foods present in the Mediterranean-style diet and the improvement of brain functions, as well as a lower rate of decline in mental health. As we age, cognitive functions decrease and this sometimes leads to extremely serious conditions such as Alzheimer's disease or the appearance of dementia.

It's also common to experience a mild memory loss and misunderstanding spells when you're older and this isn't considered a sign of a neurological disorder. The Mediterranean diet can help you to stay mentally active given your age, to fully enjoy life and potentially reduce the normal effects of aging.

7. Lower risk of cancer

It has also been linked to reducing the risk of developing and dying from certain types of cancer, in addition to all other serious diseases that the Mediterranean diet may help to reduce. Eating lots of fruits and vegetables is an important component of the diet, which is one of the reasons you can reduce your cancer risk-most fruits and vegetables are rich in antioxidants.

It is understood that antioxidants are anti-carcinogenic. Nuts and oils in the Mediterranean diet also play an important role in reducing inflammation and insulin differentiation, which may inhibit the growth of certain types of cancer.

8. Reduction of preservatives and chemicals

The Mediterranean diet is filled with fresh produce, vegetables and fruits, meats delivered straight from the butcher shop, and ocean-fresh fish. It means we do not consume precooked and processed foods that typically contain a lot of additives and preservatives that are not safe for anyone.

If you want to see something as simple as a frozen chicken package, there are usually multiple lines in the ingredient list you don't eat only chicken. In addition to salt, fat, sugar and calories, precooked foods bring other potentially harmful ingredients into your body. Any foods that can be harmful to your health will be eliminated following a Mediterranean-style diet.

9. Increased consumption of antioxidants

Antioxidants, nowadays, are a phenomenon. List after list of super-foods includes antioxidant-rich components. These have been linked to lowering the risk of certain types of cancer and the benefits don't stop there-they have natural anti-inflammatory properties and can help prevent heart disease, decrease the risk of developing diabetes and boost the immune system. They also possess anti-aging properties.

That's a fantastic list of potential benefits and eating more fresh fruits and vegetables is all you need to do. Explore the various types and stuff you've never eaten before. There's no reason I couldn't explore new food!

10. Less likely to suffer from Parkinson's disease

There is some debate as to whether or not the diet in the Mediterranean style may minimize the risk of Parkinson's disease developing, but there are enough scientists who believe that there is a link worth considering.

A study published in the American Journal of Clinical Nutrition found that the development of diseases such as Parkinson's and Alzheimer's had decreased by 13 percent when participants followed a Mediterranean diet, which is a fairly large number in general terms. The exact diet portion that reduces this risk has not been established but the facts are insight.

Losing Weight with the Mediterranean Diet

There are many different types of diets, perhaps even too many. However, experts say you should pay attention to the healthiest ones, which also provide nutrients to your body in addition to helping you lose weight. Mediterranean diet-making friends with it are worthwhile, because it is a great example of this. Don't forget this approach!

The Mediterranean diet is rich in protein, fiber, omega-3 fatty acids, whole grains, minerals, vitamins, and most importantly, it contains almost no fat, carbohydrate, and industrial flour. Let's look at it deeper.

How can a Mediterranean diet help me lose weight?

- First of all, the strict Mediterranean diet is not the same as weight loss. This diet is synonymous with the development of very healthy eating habits and thanks to the ingredients found therein, we learn to control body weight and exclude everything else that can lead to weight gain and even diseases from the diet. Nutritionists suggest you can lose weight just one kilogram a week by using this type of diet.

- In other words, the Mediterranean diet is not only helpful to us but also to our entire family. The World Health Organization (WHO) proposed the basic principles of the so-called healthy eating pyramids.

- The advantages of a Mediterranean diet are the product of the excellent quantity of healthy fats. These are just monounsaturated fats that are present in olive oil and fatty acids like Omega 3 and 6.

- That diet excludes both animal protein and red meat.

- The richest in antioxidants is the Mediterranean diet: fruits, dried fruits, vegetables and legumes.

- This contains a good amount of fiber.
- The Mediterranean diet helps to reduce cholesterol in the body, protects against cardiovascular disease and takes care of your weight due to a healthy amount of nutrients that removes unhealthy fat.

CHAPTER THREE

Starting the Mediterranean Diet

The first step in getting the Mediterranean diet started is to learn its foundations, that is, the ingredients that make it up and make it one of the world's healthiest choices.

1. Olive oil as a fat preference

Rich in vitamin E, monounsaturated fatty acids and antioxidants, the Mediterranean diet's essential oil is this. For example, it is used to season salads, fry, toast and all that needs some form of fat for seasoning or cooking!

So if you're thinking about starting the Mediterranean diet, leave the butter and heat the olive oil.

2. Daily consumption of plant foods

For their significant contribution of minerals, vitamins, fibers and antioxidants, grains, fruits, vegetables and nuts are eaten every day and regularly. However, according to the Mediterranean diet food pyramid, each main meal should include: 1-2 fruits More than 2 vegetable servings, natural or cooked. Preferably, at least one raw daily portion.

3. Daily cereal consumption

One or two portions of cereal are recommended per meal, preferably whole grain in the form of rice, pasta, bread, couscous or other types, for example. The carbohydrates derived from these foods will, of course, provide the necessary energy to face the day.

4. Choose fresh, seasonal foods

The purchasing and use of fresh and seasonal foods allow us to enjoy their nutrients, taste and fragrance. Use foods that are unprocessed and seasonal. It is a safe step and is environmentally friendly.

5. Moderate consumption of red meat

Because of the health problems that animal fat intake can create, moderate consumption of red and processed meat is recommended. Therefore, according to the Mediterranean diet, the saturated fats of these meats must be reduced.

6. Daily consumption of dairy products

Yogurt and cheese are a daily part of the Mediterranean diet and contain important minerals such as calcium and phosphorus, vitamins and proteins with a high biological value.

7. Fish two times a week and eggs, three or four

Starting with the Mediterranean diet, it's important to reduce your consumption of red meat and instead eat fish, for example, for its content of Omega-3 fatty acids and eggs, sources of quality protein.

8. Bakery and sweets products, very low consumption

It's not a matter of removing these ingredients from your diet entirely, but note that your consumption should be extremely moderate. In fact, it recommends fewer than two servings a week.

9. Water as a preferred drink

Water is a key Mediterranean diet pillar and should be your favorite drink. Furthermore, wine is also part of this diet, consumed in moderation and usual fashion.

10. Physical exercise

A good diet is not the only thing that you need to look for to enjoy good health. Therefore, n will make sure to exercise daily and regularly to enjoy the benefits of a healthy diet.

CHAPTER FOUR

Eat Well and Stay Healthy

the Mediterranean Way

The Mediterranean diet is an eating style that can help you lose weight and improve your health. Typically eaten in countries and regions bordering the Mediterranean sea, it is based on diet. This emphasizes fruits, vegetables, whole grains, and legumes while including smaller amounts of meat, poultry, dairy and sweets. Several studies have shown that the Mediterranean diet will help you lose weight and reduce the risk of heart disease, cancer, Parkinson's disease, and Alzheimer's. Adopting a lifestyle and diet in a Mediterranean style will help you eat better and stay healthy.

Adopting a Mediterranean Style Diet

Use the foods more focused on plants. Eating more plant-based foods is one of the main components of the Mediterranean diet. These types of foods will make up the majority of your diet.

Foods based on plants include a wide variety of foods— some high in protein, fiber, and many vitamins and minerals.

Most of all eat: fruits, vegetables, whole grains, nuts, peas, beans, lentils... At each meal and snack you should include one or more of those food groups.

In the Mediterranean diet nuts and seeds are especially common. These contain a large amount of protein, minerals, and heart-healthy fats. Include 1–2 table cubits per serving (14.8–29.6 ml).

Citrus fruits are another prevalent plant-based food in the Mediterranean diet. Lemons, limes, oranges, and grapefruits have large amounts of vitamin C, a potent antioxidant that has been shown.

Replace butter with heart-sanctioning oils. Another trademark of the Mediterranean diet is the use of a great deal of olive oil. It is used for cooking as well as dressing up various foods.

Butter is a less nutritious choice than olive oil, since it is very high in saturated fat. Some studies have linked higher saturated fat levels to heart disease.

On the other side, olive oil is thought to be a superior and more nutritious type of fat. It is very rich in monounsaturated fats that have been linked with reduced heart disease risk.

While olive oil is a healthier fat option, it is still fat, and should be weighed when you use it. One serving is one tablespoon and the portions should be limited to two or three per day.

Red meat limit. Red meat consumption in the US is higher than in a lot of other countries. The Mediterranean diet generally only occasionally includes red meat — perhaps once or twice a month.

Red meat was associated with a range of adverse health effects when eaten in large quantities (such as heart disease and diabetes). A study recently found that high amounts of red meat are associated with a shortened life span.

Substituting other sources of protein (such as tofu, rice, nuts, or eggs) was associated with a reduced risk of heart disease and diabetes.

Include products made with low-fat dairy. The dairy products are another great source of protein found in the Mediterranean diet. During the day throw in a serving or two of them.

Low-fat dairy contains a lot of protein but there are also high amounts of calcium, vitamin D and potassium in these foods.

Yogurt, cheeses, milk or cottage cheese may be included in dairy products.

Measure the proper serving of dairy foods. Attach 1/2 cup yogurt, 1 oz cheese, or 6 oz low-fat milk to taste.

At least eat fish twice a week. The Mediterranean diet also stresses the consumption of fish and shellfish, in addition to eating several different sources of plant-based proteins.

Most diets in the Mediterranean style recommend eating at least twice a week fish or shellfish. Include dinner with a 3-4 oz serving of fish or shellfish.

Many shellfish and fish are larger in omega-3 fats. A particular type of fat was associated with a reduced risk of heart disease, a reduction in blood pressure, cholesterol and triglyceride.

All seafood is a great choice and particularly high in heart-healthy fats are fish such as salmon, tuna, mackerel, and sardines.

Cook instead of salt, with herbs and spices. Salt improves your food's taste, but using more herbs and spices like the Mediterranean diet also adds a lot of flavor to your food without the salt added. Salt increases the risk of hypertension which can lead to heart disease or stroke. Herbs have no adverse effects, and are useful in the diet.

Basil: This herb is very rich in essential oils and phenolic compounds that have anti-inflammatory properties and can relieve chronic inflammation such as arthritis. It is also rich in beta-carotene, lutein and vitamin A, which protect the body in an exceptional way against free radicals.

Marjoram: This plant was used for a wide range of ailments including colds, symptoms of menopause relief, cramps of the stomach and gas.

Oregano: This herb was associated with reducing disorders of the respiratory tract, GI disorders, PMS symptoms, and urinary tract infections. It is also high in fatty acids such as magnesium, dietary fiber, calcium, manganese, vitamin c, A and omega-3.

Peregrine: This common herb was thought to help prevent cancer, diabetes and improve the health of bones. It also contains high quantities of vitamins A, K, and C.

Sage: In addition to potentially lowering blood glucose and cholesterol levels, this herb may reduce cognitive ailments like Alzheimer's and dementia.

Thyme: This herb may be effective against infection by fungi, especially those around your toenails. It may also help to reduce acne, high blood pressure and certain cancers.

Mint: This plant can help with digestion, alleviate seasonal allergies and prevent

Rosemary: The herb will improve the immune system and aid with digestion. It has anti-inflammatory properties that can decrease the severity of asthma attacks and increase blood flow to your brain, which can enhance cognitive problems.

Garlic: This spice has been involved in numerous health benefits such as the lower risk of heart disease and artery hardening, reducing high cholesterol, lowering the risk of heart attack and lowering the risk of high blood pressure.

Indulge in a glass of wine. In addition to raising your HDL (the "healthy" cholesterol), and preserving your coronary arteries, drinking wine in moderation will reduce your chances of developing cardiovascular diseases.

Several research studies have shown that the right amounts of wine consumption— one glass (5 oz) or less per day— have its benefits.

Wine helps dilate the arteries and increase blood flow within your body. Wine phenols also aid in reducing bad cholesterol. When you drink alcohol, try drinking one 5-ounce glass of wine per day.

Eat smaller portions. The portions that are usually served in the US are much greater than required. Large large portions, when consumed, can lead to excess calorie intake, weight gain and obesity.

Smaller portions of the Mediterranean diet include. Such smaller portions can help keep calories low and reduce weight or maintain weight.

Measure portions of all groceries. To stay on track, you can use a food scale, or weigh cups. Guessing or "eye-balling" portions usually results in larger portions than is required.

Protein foods should be 3-4 oz per serving, vegetables 1 cup or 2 cups of leafy greens, fruit 1/2 cup and grains 1/2 cup per serving as well.

Exercise regularly. People are far more involved in the countries bordering the Mediterranean than in the US. Their increased level of activity is partly the reason why they consider their lifestyle very healthy.

Physical activity has been associated with many health benefits, including increased levels of high-density lipoprotein (HDL or "healthy" cholesterol), decreased levels of triglycerides, decreased risk of diabetes and high blood pressure, enhanced arthritis-related pain, and decreased cancer rates.

Seek to do aerobic exercise of moderate intensity at least for 30 minutes during each session five days a week. This will help you meet the US minimum physical activity requirement of 150 minutes per week.

Take up walking, running, cycling, swimming, and hiking to get aerobic exercise. Include two to three days of 20-minute strength training every week.

You should also try pilates or yoga that will help build your strength and flexibility.

Walk and move more throughout the day. People living in the Mediterranean are taking part in more leisure practices compared to people living in the US. It has been shown that being more active over the day has similar benefits to aerobic activity.

Lifestyle practice is the activity that you embed in your daily routine. Taking the stairs, for example, or mopping down the concrete, are called lifestyle behaviors.

Throughout their days' Mediterranean people tend to have more activity in the lifestyle. For instance, we're cycling to and from destinations, or riding a bike instead. Involvement is an essential part of your daily routine.

Think of your day, the schedule for your work and the whole week. Where can you put in more movement or more steps? Can you ride a motorcycle to work? Can you go to the drugstore or grocery store? You should take the stairs instead of the lift? Try to incorporate more moves into your day.

Eat mindfully. Another feature of a Mediterranean diet and lifestyle is that they usually eat more carefully compared to the American hustle and bustle. Conscious eating can help eat less, enjoy eating more and even help you lose weight.

It's a way to eat carefully. It's a way to eat that makes you more aware of what kind of food you consume, how much you eat and how easily you eat.

Take 20 minutes to eat your meal, remove distractions from your dining area (e.g., TVs or cell phones), take small bites, chew more thoroughly, and adjust your body's sense of satiety.

Manage stress. Chronic lifestyle stress can be tough to deal with. Studies have shown, however, that people living in Mediterranean countries can deal with stress better and suffer less from heart disease.

Try to tackle as much tension as possible. Try to listen to music, exercise, meditate, do yoga, or converse with a friend or family member.

When stress management is too complicated, or if you are unsure how to deal with stress, see a life coach or therapist for additional assistance.

When talking about the Mediterranean diet, the evolution of the human species over the centuries must be taken into account, which has brought about many changes both in their way of life and in their relationship with the rest of the species, as well as in the transformation of their diet reflected in changes in food depending on geographical areas.

In human history there has been a long transition from prehistoric hunters and gatherers to the present day. Throughout post-industrialized societies, major changes have occurred which are also reflected in the diet and nature of human nutrition.

In different cultures it is possible to recognize certain features that make their diet a lifestyle. This is done with the popular Mediterranean diet, a diet that combines various ingredients from local agriculture through recipes and special methods of healthy cooking.

Instead of a food program, the popular and world-famous Mediterranean diet is a cultural heritage that encourages you to lead a healthy lifestyle consisting of a variety of ingredients used to prepare recipes focused on exercise in seasonal, natural, and local items with moderate physical activity.

As its name suggests, this diet is born in the villages of the Mediterranean basin, transmitted from generation to generation for centuries and changing and incorporating new techniques of food and cultivation according to the geographical location of these populations.

The Mediterranean Diet's basic ingredients make up a perfect "wheat-vine-olive" triangle to which vegetables, legumes, fruits, fish, cheeses, and nuts are added and olive oil is the main source of fats. The Mediterranean Diet offers enough macronutrients to the body through a healthy and varied diet plan.

CHAPTER FIVE

Mediterranean Diet Food Pyramid Vs Traditional Food Pyramid

For most of us, the food pyramid contains the most recognized symbol of healthy food. This demonstrates which foods we can consume in which portion size so our body gets the nutrients these needs. If you are designing a healthy diet plan you will do well to look at the pyramid of Mediterranean diet foods.

What is the Mediterranean Diet Food Pyramid?
The Mediterranean diet food pyramid is an alternative to the conventional one that is becoming increasingly popular because it is not based on popular trends in the food industry. The diet itself is centered within the Mediterranean region, on thousands of years of tradition. Mediterranean countries ' dietary traditions have long been recognized as being very healthy, and the food they eat is one of the main factors in that healthiness. Being aware of the difference between the traditional food pyramid and the Mediterranean one will help you improve your health.

The Mediterranean diet pyramid is substantially different from the traditional one we are familiar with. Several glaring discrepancies, namely;

- The Mediterranean one has no fats category Red meat Is at the top of the Mediterranean pyramid as a food to eat with sweets / desserts at least.

- Olive oil is grouped with fruit and vegetables as something to be frequently consumed

The top portion of the Mediterranean diet food pyramid starts with red meat as an animal protein source. Red meat and candy are the Mediterranean's least-eaten foods, around 2-3 times a month. The next group, eaten a few days a week, includes meat, eggs and dairy products such as cheese and yogurt. Next come fish and seafood eaten almost daily. The Mediterranean diet is basically low in saturated fats and high in monounsaturated fats, and high in omega 3.

The lower pyramid level consists of fruits, vegetables, legumes (beans), nuts, seeds, herbs, spices, whole-grain bread, whole-grain pasta, couscous, brown rice, polenta, and other whole grains. The Mediterranean people rarely eat processed grains (i.e., white flour). A wide number of these fresh foods are consumed every day, and are usually either raw or cooked slightly. Which ensures nutrients remain intact. Cooking foods actually kills or makes most nutrients indigestible. Hence eating raw or partially cooked food is always safer.

The main aspect of the Mediterranean pyramid is to prescribe six glasses of water per day and a moderate amount of wine (i.e. one glass of red wine with dinner). It is interesting to note that in the Mediterranean pyramid, olive oil is grouped with fruits and vegetables. As you can imagine, olive oil is an essential part of the Mediterranean diet and includes many dishes. While it is true that oil is high in calories, olive oil is a good, monounsaturated fat that is high in antioxidants and contains omega-3 fatty acids, so we can consume a little more as long as we don't go crazy. Monounsaturated oils like olive oil are anti-inflammatory and help with diseases like asthma and arthritis. These are also safer in the heart because Omega 3 lowers LDL ("bad") cholesterol and increases HDL ("good") cholesterol. Less natural olive oil.

You may wonder how Mediterranean people receive their iron, as they don't eat a lot of red meat. The response to this is the same as a vegetarian is. Also good sources of iron are legumes (beans) and green leafy vegetables, and the Mediterranean diet is full of these healthy foods. Nevertheless, the whole Mediterranean diet food pyramid is made up of healthy foods that ensure that those who adopt the Mediterranean diet enjoy optimal health.

How to Implement the Mediterranean Diet into Your Lifestyle

We are all involved in being lean, losing weight, getting a good diet plan, getting rid of cardiovascular and health-related illnesses. Typically, once you have a good diet plan such as the Mediterranean diet pan, the chances are that you will eventually reduce the number of calories in your body resulting in decreased heart-related issues.

The other benefits include weight shedding, fat burning and gradually slimming down. It is truly easy to implement diet plans like the Mediterranean diet plan. That's because you can't eat the gunk and bland vegetables that many people have to submit to just because they want to live longer and healthier.

You will enjoy delicious meals with the Mediterranean diet plan while still rising the chances of getting heart-related problems. Here are a few tips to help adopt the Mediterranean diet.

1. Decide on What Diet Type

Most of the people tend to worry about their diet plans consistently.

They worry if it will work if they lose weight if they can reduce their chances of dying younger as a result of heart disease and cancer and, most importantly, worry if they can keep up with their diets.

Okay, the thing is, if you really want to do this, you have to choose which choice you think works best for you.

There are two main dietary forms or regimens. You can do the form planned or the style Do-It-Yourself. It all depends on the makeup you have. For instance, some people don't like strict time tables and are more likely to fail to use them because they are instinctively opposed to things that make them feel like they're boxed in.

Though, other people find it exciting to chart a strategy and are more likely to stick to it. It all depends on the person that you are. So, whatever happens, just pick one out. If you don't know which group you're moving for, just go for one. You can always turn to the other, if you don't like it.

2. Find Recipes that Will Work for You

The taste of the people in the food is different. You need to find and stick to that which works for you. The basic components of the Mediterranean diet plan include, among others, olive oil, legumes, vegetables, nuts, grains, unprocessed carbohydrates, fish, reduced red meat consumption and saturated fat.

Now, if you just like eating them like that, then it's all right. But if you want to make it much more fun, you'd have to find recipes that work.
The South Beach Diet recipes, for example, are great and fun to cook. So, find recipes that inculcate these and which are based on the Mediterranean diet.

3. Get Creative With the Diet

Since following a few diet plans, the reason many people return to eating junk is that the diets are either dull, repetitive or lacking in flavor. So, what you should do is just go for those delicious meals. Get yourself creative with the recipes. Try something new, and something different. Chances are if you're looking well enough, you'll find lots of Mediterranean diet recipes that will last you for a whole year and more.

4. Be Disciplined

Because the Mediterranean diet is really simple to use and apply, it is hardly called a diet by some. I just see it as an alternative lifestyle and food choices that help you stay healthy and live longer. The secret, then, is discipline. Stay focused and who knows, you could just give yourself an extra 15 years of health and life.

CHAPTER SIX

Reasons Why a Mediterranean Diet in the 21st Century Is A Healthy Choice

If you're a person on a quest for a solid diet plan, you may feel exhausted a lot of the time. It is almost impossible for a person to turn on a TV set or open a newspaper in the 21st century, without being bombarded with ads for a variety of different diet plans and items.

With the vast number of diet plans, services, supplements and aids on the market, a diet plan that can and will better meet your needs now and into the future may seem almost impossible to choose. Most significantly, it can be difficult to discern whether one or the other of these different diet plans are actually a healthy path to follow. In many cases, fad diets are not really focused on the foundations of a healthy life.

When you decide what sort of diet plan or a diet plan or diet will best serve your needs and enhance your health in the future, you will want to look at the benefits that the Mediterranean diet can offer.

While there are multiple reasons why a balanced alternative is a Mediterranean diet, there are five main reasons why a good choice is a Mediterranean diet.

1. The benefits of fruits, vegetables, fiber and whole grains

Regular consumption of fresh fruit and vegetables is an important component of the Mediterranean diet. Medical experts and nutritionists generally agree that a person should eat around 5-6 servings of fresh fruit and vegetables (or steamed items) daily.

People who generally adhere to the Mediterranean diet eventually eat more than the minimum recommended amount of fruit and vegetables. As a result, nutritionists in different parts of the world have prescribed a Mediterranean-based program for its customers. Today doctors who recommend healthy eating habits to their patients often stick to the Mediterranean diet.

The Mediterranean diet contains healthy amounts of dietary fiber and whole grains, in addition to fruit and vegetables. Fiber and whole grains have proven effective in reducing heart disease incidence and certain types of cancer.

2. The benefits of olive oil - avoiding saturated fat

Many people have a simple misperception of the Mediterranean diet. The Mediterranean diet is high in fat, many people have heard. There is some reality in the definition, on some point, that the Mediterranean diet is higher in fat than some other diet programs. A person who follows the Mediterranean diet takes from fat about thirty percent of their daily calories. (Most diets advised the consumption of fat calories at a rate of approximately thirteen to fifteen percent per day. Moreover, some diets envisage the intake of animal fat.)

The vast majority of the fat a person consumes on the Mediterranean diet comes from olive oil. The fat present in the Mediterranean diet is not, in other words, the unhealthy saturated fat that can cause disease, obesity and other health concerns. Nonetheless, research has shown that there are a variety of solid benefits of olive oil consumption, including a decrease in the risk of breast cancer incidence in women.

3. Dairy in moderation

While in some cases it can be helpful to eat low-fat or non-fat dairy products, many people worldwide rely on heavy creams, eggs, and other fatty dairy products for their daily diets.

The Mediterranean diet has low milk content. All dairy products which are currently on the menu are actually low in fat. A person who consumes four eggs a week is considered an extremely heavy eater of the eggs.

4. Red Meat in Moderation

Very little red meat is included in the Mediterranean diet. This diet depends on moderate amounts of lean poultry and fresh fish when it comes to meat products. As a result, people on the Mediterranean diet have lower levels of "bad" cholesterol and higher levels of "good: cholesterol". Furthermore, thanks to the inclusion of lean and fresh fish in the diet, the members of the Mediterranean diet enjoy the antioxidant benefits present in some oils and fish products.

5. A Well Balanced Dieting Scheme

Ultimately, the Mediterranean diet is gaining worldwide acclaim from experts and adherents as it is a balanced diet program. Study after study shows that a balanced diet low in fat which includes fruit, vegetables, whole grains and lean meatworks to ensure complete health and well-being.

A weekly menu based on the Mediterranean diet

Monday
- Breakfast: Coffee with milk. Toast with goat cheese spread. Apple.
- Mid-morning: cereal bar. Natural Orange Juice
- Food: Chickpea soup. Hake meatballs stewed with potatoes. Grapes.
- Snack: Cottage cheese with sugar.
- Dinner: Swiss chard with garlic. Grilled turkey and tomato cherry skewers with couscous. Custard apple.

Tuesday
- Breakfast: Milk with cocoa powder. Whole grains
- Mid-morning: Natural pear smoothie.

- Food: Stewed green beans. Grilled chicken fillet with steamed broccoli. Pineapple Carpaccio.
- Snack: Toast with quince jam.
- Dinner: Salad with cucumber, black olives, onion, and Feta cheese. Salmon with papillote vegetables. Peach.

Wednesday

- Breakfast: Milk Crispbread with strawberry jam.
- Mid-morning: Sandwich with lettuce, tomato, and cheese. Natural grape juice.
- Food: Tomato soup. Broth rice with rabbit and artichokes. Orange.
- Snack: Seed bread with olive oil.
- Dinner: Cauliflower sauteed with bacon. Scrambled eggs with roasted mushrooms. Banana with yogurt.

Thursday

- Breakfast: Milk Olive bread with slices of tomato and virgin olive oil.
- Mid-morning: Apple compote.
- Food: Roasted red peppers with pine nuts. Grilled pork loin with mustard and rice sauce. Khaki.

- Snack: Tuna mini sandwich.
- Dinner: Vegetable cream with croutons. Fried fish. Tangerines

Friday

- Breakfast: Coffee with milk. Toast with chocolate spread.
- Mid-morning: Muesli with dried fruit.
- Food: Stewed beans. Tortilla with vegetables and peas (Campesina) with lettuce. Grapes.
- Snack: Milk. Homemade cake.
- Dinner: Sauteed Brussels sprouts with chopped almonds. Spinach, goat cheese and honey crepe with zucchini slices. Pear.

Saturday

- Breakfast: Integral cookies. Pineapple yogurt smoothie.
- Mid-morning: Appetizer: assorted montaditos.
- Food: Migas. Nice pickled with onion. Banana flambé with chocolate.
- Snack: Macedonia.
- Dinner: Two-color puree (potato and beet) gratin. Baked carrot chicken thighs. Orange.

Sunday

- Breakfast: Coffee with milk. Ensaimada
- Mid-morning: Appetizer: assorted nuts, dried fruits, and olives.
- Food: Vegetable cannelloni au gratin. Grilled duck breast with fig sauce. Orange with custard
- Snack: Apple rolled with cinnamon.
- Dinner: Fine noodle soup. Eggs stuffed with smoked salmon gratin with grated carrot. Fruit frozen yogurt.

CHAPTER SEVEN

Mediterranean breakfast recipes

- **Scrambled eggs with truffles**

Ingredients

- 100 g shrimp (peeled and cooked)
- 3 egg yolks
- 125 ml of milk
- 125 ml whipped cream

- Sea salt (from the mill)
- Pepper (white, from the mill)
- 1 tbsp truffle oil

Preparation

1. Whisk the milk, cream, egg yolk and truffle oil in a stainless steel bowl, stirring constantly with hot steam until the egg begins to freeze.
2. Roughly chop the prawns and stir into the truffle.
3. Season the truffle eggshell with freshly ground salt and pepper.

Spaghetti Omelette

Ingredients

- 5 eggs
- 150 g spaghetti
- 30 g parmesan (freshly grated)
- 30 g butter
- 1 pinch of nutmeg (grated)
- Sea salt
- Pepper

Preparation

1. Cook and strain the spaghetti according to the package as required.
2. Beat the eggs in a bowl. Stir in the parmesan and season with salt, pepper and a pinch of nutmeg.
3. Mix in cooked spaghetti and stir well.
4. Fry half of the butter in a pan and fry the pasta mixture in a golden heat without stirring.
5. Melt the remaining butter on top of the omelet. Turn the omelet over and fry the other side until crispy.
6. Portion and serve hot.

Croque Monsieur

Ingredients

- 2 eggs
- 1 pinch paprika powder
- 1 pinch of chili pepper (or grated nutmeg)
- Oil (for baking)
- 8 slices of toasted bread
- 4 slices of Gryère cheese (alternatively Emmental cheese)
- 4 slices of ham (or 8 slices of bacon)
- 200 ml of milk

Preparation

1. For the Croque Monsieur, the top half of the toast with a slice of cheese and ham or 2 slices of bacon. Cover each with a slice of bread. Mix the eggs with milk, paprika powder, chili or nutmeg on a deep plate.
2. Pour oil into a pan about finger-high and heat. Briefly turn the filled toasts in the egg-milk on both sides and bake in the hot oil on both sides with the lowest possible heat and with the lid

closed until the cheese has melted and the toasts are a nice golden yellow. Lift out and dab the Croque Monsieur well before serving.

Crab choux

Ingredients

- 250 g crabs (small, in the shell)
- 250 g flour
- 1 tbsp butter
- 4 eggs
- salt
- Vegetable oil (for baking)
- Parsley (for sprinkling)

Preparation

1. Bring the crabs in a bit of saltwater to a boil, lift them out, let them cool down and peel. Squeeze about 200 ml of cooking water through a hair strainer and bring in a saucepan to boil. Remove the butter and flour and keep simmering, stirring constantly until the dough comes off the surface. Remove the pan from the hob and continue beating the dough until it has cooled a little. Then add one egg slowly at a time and beat vigorously

again. Add crabs, and let the dough rest for 15 minutes at least. Heat oil in a large saucepan. Cut the little donuts out of the dough and bake them in hot oil, golden yellow. Lift out, drain on paper in the kitchen, and sprinkle with parsley to serve.

Greek yogurt with honeycomb

Ingredients

- 500 g yogurt (Greek)
- 150 g honeycomb
- 4 pieces of figs (fresh)
- 2 tbsp pine nuts
- Cassis syrup (black currant syrup)

Preparation

1. Peel the figs cut them into wedges and mix them with the yogurt. Roast the pine nuts, chop them and also pour them into the yogurt. Arrange yogurt in a bowl and drizzle with a little honey and cassis syrup.

Tramezzini with egg and anchovies

Ingredients

- 12 slices of tramezzini bread (soft, juicy white bread without rind)
- 6 eggs (hard-boiled and thinly sliced)
- 12 anchovy fillets (inlaid)
- 200 g mayonnaise (homemade if possible)

Preparation

1. Brush the bread slices generously with mayonnaise. The top half of the bread with half of the egg slices. Place the drained anchovy fillets on top and top with the remaining egg slices. Put the remaining bread slices on top and cut diagonally into two triangles.

Herb omelet

Ingredients

- 12 eggs
- 12 tbsp herbs (of your choice, washed, finely chopped)
- 6 tablespoons of butter
- 1 tablespoon of flour
- 1/8 l milk
- salt
- pepper
- 2 tbsp parmesan (or other hard cheese to taste)

Preparation

1. For the herbal omelet, first, melt the butter in a pan and gently braise the herbs on a low flame. Attention: The herbs must not brown at all!
2. In the meantime, stir the eggs with salt, pepper, parmesan, flour, and milk into a liquid pancake batter. Pour carefully over the herbs, stir well. When a firm crust has formed on the underside, turn the dough and bake. (Add a little butter to taste, so that the other side also becomes crispy.)
3. Arrange and serve the herb omelet on plates.

Tip

1. The herbal omelet can be eaten hot, is cut into pie-like triangles but is also perfect as a small bite with wine. The herbal omelet is also ideal as a soup inlay! In this function - a little modified and cut into small strips - it has also made a career in Viennese cuisine as a "fried soup".

Caprese Toast

Ingredients

- 1-2 paradises
- 2 pkg. Mozzarella
- 1 clove of garlic
- 4 slices of toast
- 1 tbsp pesto (basil)
- 1 tablespoon of olive oil
- Basil (fresh)
- salt
- Pepper (from the mill)

Preparation

1. For the Caprese toast, first, wash the parsnip and cut it into slices. Also, cut the mozzarella into slices. Peel garlic and chop finely.
2. Brush the toast slices with pesto and place the parsnip and mozzarella on top. Mix the garlic and olive oil and spread over them.
3. Bake the toasts with the grill function of the oven until the mozzarella melts.
4. Salt and pepper the Caprese toast before serving and garnish with fresh basil leaves.

Italian rolls ("pane arabo")

Ingredients

- 500 g of flour
- 300 g water (lukewarm)
- 1 pkg. Of dry yeast
- 1 tsp salt (coated)
- 1 tsp sugar (coated)

Preparation

1. Mix the flour, yeast, salt, sugar, and water and knead well. It should be an elastic and not sticky dough. Knead in a little more flour if necessary. Leave the dough covered until it has doubled (approx. 1 hour).
2. Divide the dough into 8 parts and roll them out with a rolling pin to round or oval rolls. Place the rolls on a baking sheet lined with baking paper and cover them with a clean kitchen towel and let them rise for another 30 minutes.
3. Preheat the oven to 250 ° C.
4. Bake the rolls for about 10-12 minutes. From the 8th minute, check again and again that the rolls are not too brown.
5. The rolls can still be served warm.

Eggs alla Saltimbocca

Ingredients

- 4 eggs
- Pepper (black, freshly ground)
- 4 slices of Parma ham
- 8 sage leaves (large)
- 2 tablespoons of olive oil
- 4 toothpicks

Preparation

1. Bring water to a boil in a saucepan and boil the eggs for 6 to 7 minutes until they are soft to the touch. Let the eggs cool, remove the shell and cut in half lengthways. Pepper the cut surfaces.
2. Halve the length of the ham and wrap a strip around half an egg.
3. Wash the sage leaves, pat dry and attach each leaf to the ham with a toothpick.
4. Heat the oil in a pan and fry the wrapped eggs over moderate heat for about 5 minutes until the ham is crispy. Turn the eggs.
5. Place two egg halves on a plate and serve immediately.

Oatmeal Seasoned with Vegetables

Instructions

- 4 cups of water
- 2 cups of "cut" oatmeal (quick-cooking steel-cut oats)
- 1 teaspoon Italian spices
- ½ teaspoon Herbamare or sea salt
- 1 teaspoon garlic powder
- 1 teaspoon onion powder
- ½ cup nutritional yeast
- ¼ teaspoon turmeric powder
- 1½ cup kale or tender spinach
- ½ cup sliced mushrooms
- ¼ cup grated carrots
- ½ cup small chopped peppers

Preparations

1. Boil the water in a saucepan.
2. Add the oatmeal and spices and lower the temperature.
3. Cook over low heat without lid for 5 to 7 minutes.
4. Add the vegetables.
5. Cover and set aside for 2 minutes.
6. Serve immediately.

Millet and flaxseed pancakes

These delicious pancakes are fluffy and popular with adults and children! Everyone keeps coming back for more. The combination of almond milk and rice vinegar creates the buttery taste that people crave.

Instructions

- 3 cups oatmeal
- ½ cup of millet flour
- ½ cup ground flax seeds
- 1 teaspoon of sea salt
- 1½ teaspoon baking soda
- 2 teaspoons baking powder
- 4 cups vanilla almond milk
- 2 tablespoons rice vinegar
- 1 tablespoon maple honey or date paste
- 1 tablespoon pure vanilla extract
- 3 tablespoons unsweetened applesauce

Preparations

1. Mix the dry ingredients in a bowl.
2. In a different bowl, mix the liquid ingredients.
3. Pour the liquid ingredients over the dry ones and combine them well.

4. Process the mixture well in a blender until smooth and lump-free.
5. Heat a pan over medium-low heat.
6. Using a ladle, pour the desired amount of mixture into the pan.
7. Turn the pancake when bubbles appear on the top, and underneath it is firm for approximately 5 minutes.

Millet and buckwheat muffins with black currants

Ingredient

- ½ cup (90 g) of millet
- ½ cup (80 g) of unroasted buckwheat groats
- 4 chopped figs
- ¾ cup (160 ml) oatmeal or rice milk
- 1 tablespoon applesauce
- 1 heaped tablespoon (40 g) peanut butter
- 1 large ripe banana
- 1 pinch of sea salt
- 2 heaped teaspoons of baking powder
- ¾ cup (100 g) blackcurrants, fresh or frozen

Preparations

1. Dip millet and buckwheat overnight (or all day) in separate containers. Wash and drain (a filter can be used).
2. Soak the chopped figs in ¾ cup (160 ml) of oat milk for at least 30 minutes.
3. Heat the oven to 300-350 ° F (177 ° C).
4. Put the ingredients, except baking powder and blackcurrants, in a blender and mix them until a homogeneous lump is formed without

lumps. Do not worry; It is supposed to be quite liquid since millet inflates considerably.

5. Now mix the baking powder. Unplug the blender and finally combine (DON'T LIQUID) the currants with a spoon.

6. Divide the dough into 9 muffin pans and bake for 33 to 35 minutes, until golden brown.

Apple and pumpkin pie

Ingredient

- 1 spoon ground flax seeds + 2 ½ tablespoons water (flax egg)
- ½ cup all-purpose gluten-free flour (or oatmeal)
- 1 ½ cup quick-cooking oatmeal
- 1 tablespoon baking powder
- 1 teaspoon baking soda
- 2 tablespoons pumpkin pie spice
- 1 tablespoon cinnamon
- 4 medium granny smith apples
- ½ cup date pasta
- 1 cup pumpkin puree
- 1 teaspoon vanilla extract
- ¼ cup of water (optional)

Preparations

1. Preheat the oven to 350 degrees F.
2. Mix ground flaxseed (flax) seeds with water in a small bowl and set aside for 10 minutes.
3. Mix all dry ingredients in a large bowl.
4. Cut the apples into thin slices and place them in a container.

5. Add the pumpkin puree, vanilla extract, flaxseed with water, and date paste to apples and mix well.
6. merge the dry ingredients with the apples and mix well. Add water if the mixture seems to be too dry.
7. Place the mixture in an 8 x 11 (2 quarts) container suitable for baking and bake for 30-35 minutes.

Pumpkin and oatmeal bars

Ingredient

- 3 cups thick oatmeal
- 1 cup seedless dates
- ½ cup of boiling water
- 2 teaspoons pumpkin pie spice
- 1 tablespoon ground flaxseed or chia seeds
- ¼ cup small sliced nuts (optional)
- ¼ cup of vegetable milk
- 1 cup mashed pumpkin

Preparations

1. Preheat the oven to 350 degrees Fahrenheit.
2. Cut the date into small pieces, put them in a bowl, and pour hot water. Rest for 10 minutes.
3. Add dry ingredients to the bowl and mix well.
4. Add dates to the dry ingredients along with water, pumpkins, and plant milk and mix well.
5. Cover the square bread with baking paper and push the mixture firmly into the bread.
6. Cook for 15-20 minutes.
7. Allow the mixture to cool completely in the container, then cut into 16 squares or 8 large bars.

8. Store in the refrigerator for up to 7 days.

Blackberry and lemon muffins for tea

Ingredient

- 2 cups whole grain wheat flour for baking
- ½ cup of Sucanat (refined cane sugar)
- 1½ teaspoon baking powder
- 1 teaspoon grated lemon peel
- ½ cup natural soy yogurt
- 1 cup non-dairy milk
- 1 tablespoon lemon juice
- 2 egg substitutes (2 tablespoons ground flaxseed with 6 tablespoons water)
- 1 cup blackberries
- 2 tablespoons coconut with reduced-fat and sugar-free content (optional)

Preparation

1. Preheat to 350 ° F (177 ° C) in the oven.
2. Fill a paper-coated mold for 12 muffins (or use a non-stick skillet).
3. In a medium bowl, mix flour, sucanat sweetener, baking powder, and rubbed lemon peel.

4. In a separate bowl, mix soy yogurt, milk, lemon juice, and egg substitutes.
5. Pour into the dry mixture the wet mixture and stir until it is hot.
6. Carefully add blackberries.
7. In the prepared muffin pan, distribute the mixture evenly.
8. Sprinkle the coconut (optional) on top of the muffins.
9. Bake them for 45 minutes in the preheated oven or until one of them has a toothpick inserted in the middle. Until serving, let them cool slightly.

Cocoa, banana, and whole-grain spelled flour muffins

Ingredient

- 2 large bananas (I use frozen bananas and then defrost them)
- 2 cups whole grain spelled flour
- 1 cup walnuts, chopped into large pieces
- ½ cup raw cocoa powder
- ¼ cup applesauce
- 1 cup almond milk
- ¼ cup maple syrup, 100% pure
- ½ teaspoon baking powder

Preparations

1. Preheat the oven to 300-350 ° F (177 ° C).
2. Line the muffin pan with baking paper.
3. Crush the bananas in a large bowl.
4. Add the almond milk, maple syrup, applesauce, and mix them.
5. Add whole-grain spelled flour, baking powder, and cocoa powder and mix them.
6. Add the chopped walnuts.
7. Pour the mixture into muffin pans.

8. Cook the muffins for about 25 minutes or until when a skewer is inserted, it is clean.

Oatmeal and Apple Muffins

Ingredient

- 1 cup unsweetened applesauce
- ¼ to ½ cup of seedless dates
- 1 cup oat milk (you can use another non-dairy milk)
- Egg substitute (2 tablespoons of flaxseed mixed with 6 tablespoons of water)
- 1 tablespoon apple cider vinegar
- ½ cup unrefined sugar
- 1 teaspoon cinnamon
- 1 ½ cups oat flakes
- ½ cup raisins
- 1½ cup whole grain wheat flour
- ¾ teaspoon baking soda
- 1 teaspoon baking powder

Preparations

1. The oven should be preheated to 300-375 ° F (191 ° C).

2. Puree with 1/4 to 1/2 cup of seedless dates with 1 cup of applesauce (depending on the desired sweetness).

3. Mix the linseed with water in a large bowl. Applesauce, milk, sugar, raisins, and vinegar are added; blend well. Add the oatmeal, stir and set aside until all is combined.

4. Place the flour, baking soda, and baking powder into a separate bowl. Apply it to the mixture of apple and oatmeal and whisk until all is combined.

5. Pour the mixture into a lightly oiled silicone muffin mold with a spoon. (If you're using a regular muffin pan, cupcake papers should be used).

6. Bake the muffins till they are ready for 20 to 25 minutes.

Pear and hazelnut crostini

Ingredients

- 4-8 slices of spelled bread (or baguette)
- 3 pears (Good Helene)
- 2 tbsp hazelnuts (chopped)
- 200 g yogurt (Greek)
- 3 tbsp maple syrup
- lemon balm

Preparation

1. First, stir in the yogurt with 2 tablespoons of maple syrup. Wash, peel, core and cut the pears into thin slices.
2. Toast bread slices or fry them in a pan with olive oil.
3. Brush the bread with yogurt, top with the pear slices and sprinkle with the hazelnuts and lemon balm.
4. Drizzle the remaining maple syrup over the pear and hazelnut crostini and serve the crostini.

Feta and olive pancakes with bird salad

Ingredients

For the salad:

- 1 cup (s) bird salad (washed and dried)
- 3 tbsp cashew nuts (roasted)
- Apple Cider Vinegar
- olive oil
- sea-salt
- Pepper (from the mill)

For the pancakes:

- 100 g milk
- 200 g yogurt (Greek)
- 1 tbsp baking powder
- 1 tsp soda
- 150 g flour (smooth)
- 3 eggs
- 3 tbsp olives (black, chopped)
- 2 sprig (s) of thyme (leaves plucked)
- 100 g feta (crumbled)
- sea-salt
- Pepper (from the mill)
- Olive oil (for frying)

Preparation

1. Stir the milk, butter, baking powder, baking soda, flour and eggs for the pancakes first with feta olive pancakes and bird salad. Remove the olives, feta and thyme and season with salt and pepper.
2. In a saucepan heat the olive oil and fry the pancake mixture in 3 to 4 portions (thaler should not be too large). Turn and bake for 1 minute once bubbles have formed.
3. Mix the bird salad and the cashew nuts, season with a little vinegar of apple cider, olive oil, sea salt and pepper.
4. Mount the pancakes into a tower and serve with bird salad on the feta olive pancakes.

Bruschetta with mozzarella

Ingredients

- 1/4 kg tomatoes (diced)
- 2 cloves of garlic (finely chopped)
- 1 pinch of salt
- some pepper
- 1 pinch paprika powder
- 1-2 mozzarella
- 1 handful of basil (chopped)
- some olive oil
- 1 loaf (s) of ciabatta (cut into slices approximately thumb-wide)
- some sugar

Preparation

1. For the bruschetta with mozzarella, fry the tomatoes and garlic in a hot pan with olive oil.
2. Season with salt, pepper, paprika powder, sugar, and basil and let it brew for another 5 minutes.
3. Place the hot bruschetta on the ciabatta, place the finely chopped mozzarella on top and let it melt and garnish with basil.

Greek omelet

Ingredients
- 4 eggs
- 150 g feta
- 2 tablespoons of olive oil
- Oregano (dried)
- Chives (finely chopped)
- Basil leaves (fresh)

Preparation

1. For the Greek omelet, pat the feta cheese dry with kitchen paper and cut into small cubes or crumble.
2. Pour oil into the hot pan and add whisked eggs. Then sprinkle the chopped feta cheese evenly over it.
3. Slowly slow down on a low flame, sprinkle with dried oregano. Divide the omelet in half, fold it together and sprinkle with chives on the plates.
4. Decorate with fresh basil leaves. Serve with bread and salad. Be sure to have pepper and salt grinder at the table.

Masabacha green lentil curry

Ingredients

- 3 tablespoons of extra virgin olive oil
- 1 small onion, finely diced
- 1 ½ teaspoon of chopped garlic
- ⅔ cup of green lentils, rinsed
- ⅔ cup of red lentils, rinsed
- 2 cups of low-sodium no-chicken or chicken broth
- 1-2 cups of water, divided
- 1 ½ teaspoon of curry powder
- 1 medium-sized carrot, roughly grated
- ¼ teaspoon of kosher salt
- ¼ teaspoon of ground pepper
- 1 cup of thinly sliced arugula
- 2 tablespoons of finely chopped red onion
- 1 jalapeño pepper, sliced
- ⅔ cup of tahini
- 1 ½ teaspoon of chopped garlic
- ½ cup of ice water
- ¼ cup of lemon juice
- ¼ teaspoon of kosher salt

Preparation

1. Heat oil over medium heat, in a medium saucepan. Add the onion and cook, stirring for 5 to 8 minutes, until tender and translucent. Add the garlic and cook for 1-3 minutes, stirring. Add lentils, broth, 1 cup water, and curry powder, green and red. After high heat brings to a boil. Reduce heat to cook for 15 minutes and keep a simmer.

2. Stir in carrot and cook, stirring occasionally and add 2 tablespoons of water at a time if appropriate, until the green lentils are tender and the red lentils have broken down, 20 to 25 minutes more. Put away from heat, and add salt and pepper to taste. Cover. Cover.

3. Meanwhile, to prepare tahini sauce: in a mini food processor, combine tahini and garlic. In a slow stream add ice water with the motor running. Process, about 1 minute, until the tahini is light and fluffy. Add lemon juice and salt; process for about 30 seconds, until smooth.

4. Divide the lentil mixture on each plate between 4 plates, and dollop 2 tablespoons of tahini sauce. Arugula, red onion, and jalapeño top the lentils.

Serve with the additional tahini sauce, if you wish.

Mushroom olive frittata

Ingredients

- 1 tablespoon of olive oil
- 1 cup of sliced fresh cremini mushrooms
- 2 cups of roughly chopped fresh Swiss chard or spinach
- 1 large shallot, cut into thin slices
- 4 eggs
- 2 proteins
- 2 teaspoons of sliced fresh rosemary or 1/2 teaspoon of dried rosemary, crushed
- ¼ teaspoon of ground black pepper
- ⅛ teaspoon of salt
- ¼ cup of thinly sliced kalamata olives
- ⅓ cup of grated parmesan

Preparation

1. Cover broiler with preheating. Heat the oil over medium heat in a broiler-proof medium-nonstick skillet. Add mushrooms to skillet; cook, stirring occasionally, for 3 minutes. Add shallot and Swiss chard. Cook, stirring occasionally, about 5 minutes or until mushrooms and chard are tender.

2. Alternatively, whisk the seeds, egg whites, rosemary, pepper and salt together in a medium bowl. Pour egg mixture into skillet over vegetables. Cook at medium heat. Run a spatula around the bottom of the skillet as mixture sets, raising the mixture of eggs so that the uncooked part flows below. Continue cooking and edge lifting until the egg mixture is fully set, and the surface is only slightly moist.

3. Sprinkle with olives; cheese on top. Broil about 2 minutes or until the top is lightly browned and center is set. Let stand, before serving, for 5 minutes.

Broccoli-cheddar quiche with a sweet potato crust

Ingredients

- 3 ¼ cups of sliced sweet potato (approx. 1 large)
- 1 large egg, lightly beaten
- 2 tablespoons of grated parmesan
- ¼ teaspoon of salt
- ⅛ teaspoon of pepper
- 2 cups of broccoli florets
- ¾ cup of grated cheddar cheese
- 3 tablespoons of chopped shallots
- 4 large eggs
- 1 tablespoon of sour cream
- 1 cup of low-fat milk
- ¼ teaspoon of salt
- ⅛ teaspoon of pepper

Preparation

1. Preheat oven to 400 degrees F to prepare the crust. Coat with cooking spray, a9-inch deep-dish pie pan. In a medium bowl, whisk together sweet potato, 1 egg, Parmesan, 1/4 teaspoon salt and 1/8 teaspoon pepper. Move the mixture to the prepared pan and press it evenly to the bottom

of the pan and to the sides. Bake for about 25 minutes, until the crust is set and begin to brown around the edges.

2. Evenly scatter broccoli, cheddar and shallots over the crust to prepare to fill and bake a quiche. In a small bowl, whisk eggs and sour cream, until smooth. Whisk in milk, pepper and salt. Pour the egg mixture over the other ingredients for the filling. Reduce the Oven to 350 degrees F. Bake the quiche until the filling is in the center and start browning slightly, for 35 to 45 minutes. Until serving to allow to cool slightly.

Zucchini and oatmeal muffins

Ingredient

- 1 tablespoon ground chia seeds
- 3 tablespoons of water
- 1 cup unsweetened almond milk
- 1 tablespoon lemon juice
- 1 teaspoon vanilla
- 1 cup gluten-free flour mix (for example, from the Trader Joe brand)
- ¾ cup gluten-free oatmeal (create yours by grinding oat flakes in the blender)
- ½ cup flaked gluten-free oatmeal
- ½ cup unprocessed or unrefined sugar (for example, Sucanat or turbinado)
- 2 teaspoons baking powder
- 1 teaspoon baking soda
- 1 teaspoon pumpkin pie spice
- ½ teaspoon of sea salt
- 1 ½ cups grated zucchini
- ½ cup raisins
- ½ cup walnuts, chopped

Preparations

1. Preheat the oven to 350 ° F (177 ° C)

2. Line a mold for 12 muffins with paper coverings.

3. In a small bowl, combine the ground chia seeds with water and let the mixture stand.

4. In a medium bowl, combine the almond milk with the lemon juice and let the mixture stand. Don't panic if it starts to set - you are supposed to!

5. Mix the flours, corn flakes, sugar, baking powder, baking soda, salt and pumpkin pie spice in a large bowl.

6. Add vanilla and chia seeds to the almond milk and lemon juice mixture and beat until everything is combined.

7. Add the wet ingredients to the dry ones and mix them until they are combined.

8. Add zucchini, raisins, and nuts. Let the dough rest for 5-10 minutes before filling the muffin pan.

9. Cook everyone from 21 to 23 minutes. Once the muffins have come out of the oven, wait 2-3 minutes before transferring them to the rack to cool them.

CPSIA information can be obtained
at www.ICGtesting.com
Printed in the USA
BVHW040607120521
607043BV00002B/587